Math, Science and Engineering:
It's for Everyone!

by Serita Acker

Illustrated by Amina Yaqoob

Published by
Hadassah's Crown Publishing, LLC
Simpsonville, SC

ISBN 978-1-950894-67-3

Printed in the United States

Copies of the book were first made possible by Programs for Educational Enrichment and Retention and Women in Science and Engineering at Clemson University, The College of Engineering, Computing and Applied Sciences.

This book is dedicated to all the students who have crossed my path in PEER and WISE in the College of Engineering, Computing and Applied Sciences.

To the PEER and WISE Team Members: Maegan Hinson, Beth Anne Johnson, Lisa Jackson, Jodi Redlinger, Francene Thomas and Brittany Sanders. You do amazing work!

Special Acknowledgements: Katelyn Franck and Corrina Laird, for assisting with updates contained in this book and the title. Also, to Maegan Hinson for providing entry requirements for engineering programs. To James Orlick, who always did an amazing job finding funds for our STEM initiatives to build pathways for all students.

Foreword

I have promoted STEM career pathways for over 28 years at Clemson University. I love empowering all students to reach their career goals. It is my hope that this book will offer parents and educators a basic knowledge of occupations available to students with degrees in STEM majors.

The objective of *Math, Science and Engineering: It's for Everyone!* is to create an awareness of STEM fields. The focus is on everyone seeing themselves in a non-traditional career path.

Serita Acker, Executive Director
**Programs for Educational Enrichment and Retention (Peer) and
Women in Science and Engineering (WISE)**

Introduction

There are many career opportunities available in the fields of engineering, science and mathematics for students. Early exposure is vital. We must demonstrate to students how math, science and engineering personally affect their everyday lives.

In this book, you will find ways to inform students that the items they use daily are produced by engineers and/or scientists, and that math is a critical component of both fields. Products are created by skilled professionals in technical disciplines. Everyone deserves to be a part of the exciting developmental process.

It is imperative that we educate students to let them know that there are no longer any barriers between them and the fields they wish to choose. Career choices are based on interest, motivation, ability and, most of all, the drive to reach a goal.

That doesn't mean that we don't have some work to do in opening up these options to everyone. Many youths are choosing to prepare for these exciting and lucrative careers.

Careers

Notes to Parents and Educators

"Only about 18% of high school seniors perform at or above proficiency in science subjects, according to the National Math and Science Initiative. These alarming numbers are forcing America to go back to the chalkboard and evaluate where we stand in an evolving STEM world."
https://www.nymetroparents.com/article/Why-STEM-Education-Is-Important-For-All-Kids-Boys-And-Girls

"Overall, since 1990, employment in STEM occupations has grown 79%—increasing from 9.7 million to 17.3 million."
(2018 article from Pew)

"STEM education creates critical thinkers, increases science literacy, and enables the next generation of innovators."
https://www.engineeringforkids.com/about/news/2016/february/why-is-stem-education-so-important-/#:~:text=STEM%20stands%20for%20science%2C%20technology,every%20part%20of%20our%20lives.&text=STEM%20activities%20provide%20hands%2Don,much%20more%20than%20just%20learn.

Objective
The objective of *Math, Science and Engineering: It's for Everyone!*™ is to create an awareness of the technology and mathematics underlying the everyday objects in our world. The focus is on youth from elementary school to high school.

"Math, Science and Engineering" sounds very serious, right? But the products created by people who work in these fields can be a lot of fun. Besides, some of them you really couldn't do without.

I know you are wondering how that can be. Well, let me explain. Are you ever curious about how things are made or how they work?

Many people do not know that everyday items are discovered or created by mathematicians, scientists and engineers. Let's see how the fields of engineering, science and math can affect your everyday life.

MATHEMATICIANS

First of all, what do mathematicians do?

They solve problems by using numbers and formulas. Math is involved in just about everything we do. Math has given the world time, distance, weight, money, computers and much more. It makes life easier, more manageable and more orderly.

Mathematician Median Annual Salary: $110,860

SCIENTISTS

What do scientists do? They study and research the "why's" and "how's" of life. They may work in many different areas of science. Of course, they use math to report their findings.

Scientist Median Annual Salary: $91,510

Textile Scientists

One type of scientist is a textile scientist. *Textile* is another word for *fabric*. Do you like to wear the latest fashions? What about those designer jeans that everyone is wearing? Do you create your own style or set your own trends? Have you ever thought about having your name on a clothing line?

The materials, such as cotton, fabrics, fibers and film used to produce jeans, shirts and sneakers are developed and tested by textile scientists. A textile scientist might make a new fiber that won't stain or wrinkle. They might test one to be sure it is safe to use.

Of course, they use math every day. Math is also used when the product is ready to sell to measure how much fabric is produced and how many yards can be made without damaging the environment. You could be involved in this process as a textile scientist.

Textile Scientist Median Annual Salary: $83,360

Biologists, Geologists and Physicists

Biologists study the origin and development of plants, insects, animal and human life. Biology covers a broad area within the life sciences. Biologists, also called biological scientists or life scientists, can specialize in various areas.

Are you interested in the Earth's treasures, such as rocks, sand, volcanoes and the history of the Earth?

Geologists study the history of the Earth's crust. They apply knowledge of chemistry, physics, biology and mathematics to explain their findings.

Does it fascinate you how planes stay in the air or how a ball bounces up and down? Physicists study the interactions of matter and energy. Usually, they work in research laboratories and observatories.

Biologists Median Annual Salary:	$85,290
Geologists Median Annual Salary:	$93,580
Physicists Median Annual Salary:	$129,850

ENGINEERS

Who are engineers? They are people who invent ways to make life easier by using various mathematical equations and scientific applications.

Do you use lip balm, lotions or toothpaste? Do you ever think about what goes into the products you use on your hair, like shampoo?

Chemists and Chemical Engineers

Persons in these careers create products by testing and mixing various compounds and chemicals that enhance our looks and are safe for our bodies. These products are fun! They make us look and feel beautiful.

A chemist or chemical engineer might also develop new kinds of plastics, foods and medicines. Of course, they use math to measure and predict the amount of chemicals needed and to analyze their results.

| Chemist Median Annual Salary: $79,300 |
| Chemical Engineer Median Annual Salary: $108,540 |

Electrical Engineers

When you chat with your friends on a cell phone, do you ever think about how that phone works? What about your laptop? Ever wonder what's going on inside of these items? Ever wonder what's going on inside your TV when you're watching a hit movie?

These items were designed by electrical engineers. An electrical engineer is responsible for designing the currents and power sources that make your gadgets work. Of course, they use math to measure and calculate the amount of power needed to make the items work properly.

Where else does the electrical engineer use math? Did you know that applied algebra is used for technology functions on many of our devices? It helps provide clear communication on cell phones. It is also used to create UPC symbols and barcodes so that you are charged for the correct item at the supermarket.

Electrical Engineer Median Annual Salary: $100,830

Computer Scientists and Computer Engineers

Do you enjoy surfing the web or social media platforms such as Instagram or Facebook? How about playing video games?

These careers help make these items work. A computer scientist works with software and computer-based applications that operate for your enjoyment. A computer engineer works with hardware and the design of computers. And guess what? They use math to write computer programs.

| Computer Scientists Median Annual Salary: $126,830 |
| Computer Engineer Median Annual Salary: $119,560 |

Bioengineers

You probably enjoy running, playing soccer or football, dancing, swimming and other activities that require a healthy body. Our health is very important to us. At times, due to sickness or accidents, we may need help to make our bodies work properly again.

Bioengineers are among the people who may help. A bioengineer uses engineering and scientific principles to solve problems related to the health and well-being of people. They have the opportunity to work with doctors, nurses and other medical professionals.

A bioengineer is qualified to use their knowledge of mathematics, biological and physical sciences and engineering to solve problems related to the processing of various materials. They may help design bone and tissue replacements for a person who is hurt or design a new heart valve. They may assist with plastic surgery. This could include vaccine research in the fight against diseases or viruses, such as COVID-19 or other life-threatening diseases. In all of this research, they use math to measure and evaluate their work.

Bioengineer Median Annual Salary: $100,830

Picture yourself riding your bike on a beautiful, sunny day. Now think about the future when you'll probably be driving a car. Maybe you'll even fly an airplane!

Mechanical Engineers

Mechanical engineers are involved in making items that move. They build cars, airplanes, even toys, that require movement. And of course, they use math to determine the measurements and angles of movement for all these items.

Mechanical Engineer Median Annual Salary: $90,160

Do you like traveling to large cities and admiring the tall buildings? Do you enjoy visiting amusement parks or county fairs? Have you ever driven across a huge bridge? Do you notice the traffic signs and lights that let us know where we are and keep us safe when traveling?

Civil Engineers

This profession uses math to determine how tall, wide or long structures should be. Civil engineers use math to decide how fast the roller coaster should travel and how many stop signs and traffic lights we need to avoid car accidents.

Civil Engineer Median Annual Salary: $101,840

What do you think about when you plan a party? What time will the party take place? Who will you invite? What will you serve? What kind of activities will you have for your guests? What time will the party end? When you think about these details, you are organizing the party and planning for the materials you will need to make it a success.

Industrial Engineers

Industrial engineers plan and organize how a company will complete its work. They determine how items are produced. They decide how much time it will take to produce the items. They calculate how many workers their company will need.

They make sure that operations stay on schedule. They ensure their company produces the right quantities and that the products are produced correctly. They use math in all of these decisions.

Industrial Engineer Median Annual Salary: $88,950

Ceramic Engineers

Have you ever had to get braces when you visited the dentist?
Who made the material? Ceramic engineers create objects from
inorganic and non-metallic materials. They may design new
braces or retainers to straighten your teeth. They make materials
used by dental technicians to create biocompatible, lifelike dental
restorations, such as crowns, bridges and veneers. Ceramic
engineers also make ceramic materials we use in our homes.
They use math to determine these structures.

Ceramic Engineer Median Annual Salary: $95,640

Environmental Engineers

The next time you take a walk in a public park or run and play at the beach, you might want to think about who keeps those places clean and beautiful.

Environmental engineers help to ensure that we enjoy the outdoors. They make sure the air we breathe, the water we drink and swim in and the foods we eat are safe for us. They also ensure that the environment is safe for plants and animals. They are concerned with how the natural environment affects our quality of life. They use math to determine the level of dangerous chemicals in the water or air.

Environmental Engineer Median Annual Salary: $92,120

Do you love beautiful gardens and plants? Are you interested in how they grow? Are you curious about animals and insects? Are you interested in clean water? You can work with many different companies to protect the Earth and its inhabitants. And of course, you use math to calculate various questions related to the sustainability of our world.

Biosystems Engineers

Biosystems engineers are qualified to use their knowledge of mathematics, biological and physical sciences and engineering to solve problems relating to the processing of various materials.

Biosystems Engineer Median Annual Salary: $92,620

MEDICAL PROFESSIONALS

Doctors

Sometimes engineers attend medical school. Doctors practice medicine to help maintain or restore physical and mental health. They interact with patients, diagnose medical problems and treat illnesses or injuries.

Doctor Median Annual Salary:	$208,000

Nurses

Nurses provide and coordinate patient care with doctors. They diagnose and treat injuries or illnesses and aid in patients' health maintenance. And of course, they use math to determine treatments to improve health.

Nurse Median Annual Salary: $75,330

All of these fields enhance our lives and make the world we live in a better place. You can find all kinds of people in all the math, science and engineering fields. These careers ARE for everyone!

In 2013, only 0.4% of undergraduate enrollment in engineering identified as Native American and only 0.2% as Pacific Islander. Asian and Black enrollment in engineering remains below 10 percent.
https://www.nsf.gov/statistics/2017/nsf17310/static/data/tab2-9.pdf

In 2015, individuals with disabilities filled only 8% of science and engineering occupations.
https://www.nsf.gov/statistics/2017/nsf17310/static/data/tab9-8.pdf

Men who identify as gay, bisexual or "other" appear to be 12% less likely to have completed a bachelor's degree in a STEM field compared to heterosexual men.
https://www.openaccessgovernment.org/lgbtq-people-in-stem/98054/

Websites for Students

Clemson University PEER/WISE
https://www.clemson.edu/cecas/departments/peer-wise/

Extreme Science
http://www.extremescience.com/

National Geographic Kids
https://kids.nationalgeographic.com/

FabFems
https://www.fabfems.org/

KidsAhead
http://kidsahead.com/

Science Bob
https://sciencebob.com/

Sci Girls
https://pbskids.org/scigirls/

SciJinks *It's All About Weather*
https://scijinks.gov/

Scratch | *Create stories, games and animations*
https://scratch.mit.edu/

Expanding Your Horizons STEM Conferences
https://techbridgegirls.org/index.php?id=466

The Adventures of Josie True
http://www.josietrue.com/

Alice | *Virtual Environment Creation and Animation*
http://www.alice.org/

Carnegie STEM Girls
http://www.braincake.org/default.aspx

Groovy Lab in a Box
https://www.groovylabinabox.com/whats-in-the-box/how-it-works/

Apps for Students

- KaleidaCam

- Bridge Constructor

- Beaker

- Goldie Blox | Coding

- Nancy Drew Codes and Clues Mystery

- Marco Polo Weather

- Pocket Universe

- Plant Life - Science for Kids

- Mammals by Tinybop

- Cat Physics

- Move the Turtle | Learn to Code

- The Robot Factory

- Crazy Gears

- Khan Academy

Career Reflections

Use the lines on the next page for your reflections.

What hobbies do I enjoy?

What courses do I excel at?

What majors do I find most interesting?

What classes do I need to take to prepare for this major?

Is there someone I can contact to learn more about their career path?

Are there new and exciting career options in this field?

What are areas where I would like to grow to reach my goals?

Have I spoken to my parents, teachers or counselors about my interests?

Where can I find scholarships?

Career Empowerment

Write positive affirmations about yourself.

I am (Write your full name.)

_____

I am very… (ex. smart, capable, gifted)

_____

I love to (List your hobbies.)

_____

I am interested in this career path....

_____

I will learn more about...

_____

Affix a picture in the frame of you doing something you love.

Notes to Parents and Educators

Be Prepared

Below is a list of high school courses that will prepare your child or student for STEM majors in college. These courses are highly recommended, and the more they take the more they will be prepared.

4 Years of Math
- Geometry
- Calculus
- Trigonometry

3 Years of Sciences
- Biology
- Chemistry
- Physics

1 Year of Computing
- Introduction to Programming

Preparing your child for college is no easy task. There are so many considerations, not to mention knowing at what age to begin preparing them. Below we have prepared tips to help you ensure your child is ready for that big day when it comes. You will find helpful information on everything from career exploration and summer camps to SAT prep and college visits.

Set Goals

Talk with your child about setting goals, both academically and socially. Encourage them to set goals to reach their full potential. Middle school is a time of social challenges, so make sure to check in to keep them motivated and focused.

Take on the Challenge

Encourage your child to take classes that are challenging. It is important to start planning for the future by enrolling your child in the most challenging math and science courses for which they are eligible (i.e., Algebra 1, Geometry, Physical Science, etc.). Talk with teachers and counselors to make a plan that will serve your child best and help them reach their goals.

Get Involved

Talk with your child about their hobbies, clubs and other groups in which they can participate. Extracurricular activities help students find deeper meaning in their work and stay engaged in school.

Make a Plan

Talk with your child about deadlines and tests coming up. Make it a point to check in regularly about schoolwork and their grades.

Meet with a Counselor

Talking with a counselor is an important part of planning for the future. Based on your student's current classes, what comes next? Ask the counselor what course options your student has in relation to their career goals. Make sure your student continues to be challenged academically.

Career Exploration

Share about your own career and talk with your child about career options. Talk about their interests and see where those may align with potential occupations.

Summer Programs

Look for summer outreach programs and camp opportunities to keep your student engaged over the break. There are many colleges that offer camps related to different interests and hobbies.

College Search

Begin discussing college options and places where your student may want to further their education. It may be helpful to start in state and see what colleges are close to home. You can also look for colleges that offer programs related to your student's interest and schedule tours.

Work with your student to make a college wish list. Discuss the size of the school, the majors offered and the location, to begin with. You should also begin looking at the cost of college. Check out our financial aid page for types of assistance.

For more information, visit our website at

https://www.clemson.edu/cecas/departments/peerwise/prospective_students/parent-tips.html

About the Author

Serita Acker earned a bachelor's degree from Lander University and a Master of Education in Human Resource and Development from Clemson University. Before becoming the PEER/WISE Director in August 2015, Serita was Director of the Women in Science and Engineering Program. Additionally, she has more than 25 years of experience in higher education, both in the areas of student support services, mentoring and diversity programs. She is a certified Global Career Development Facilitator and Life Coach. Serita sees the PEER/WISE program's main role as providing student success programs and services that equip students with resources to excel at Clemson University and to achieve their educational goals for success after graduation.

Serita has received state and national awards including:

- College of Engineering Exceptional Staff Member
- Thomas Green Clemson Award
- Woman of Distinction by the Girl Scouts of Mountains to Midlands
- The James E. Bostic Diversity and Inclusive Excellence Award in 2017 as a Diversity Champion at Clemson University
- Clemson University Woman of the Year
- Martin Luther King, Jr. Award
- Clemson University Board of Trustees Award
- Women in Engineering Pro-Active Network Distinguished Service Award
- Career Communications Magazine College Level Promotion of Education Award

- National Association of Multicultural Engineering Advocates Award
- Upstate Diversity Award, Calder D. Elhmann Outstanding Individual.

Serita was also featured on the cover of *Insight into Diversity,* a national magazine, September 2018 edition, for her work at Clemson University. She has served as MentorLinks Consultant for the American Association of Community Colleges in Washington, DC, and she sits on many state and national boards to promote STEM. She currently serves as the National Society of Black Engineers Student Chapter Campus Advisor at Clemson University. In her spare time, she enjoys reading and traveling with her husband, Ron. They have two daughters who are both Clemson University graduates.

Sources

https://www.bls.gov/ooh/

https://careers.stateuniversity.com/pages/388/Biologist.html

https://www.census.gov/library/stories/2021/01/women-making-gains-in-stem-occupations-but-still-underrepresented.html
Statistic from 2019, article from Jan 2021

https://www.builtbyme.com/statistics-facts-women-in-stem/
Statistic from 2018, article from 2019

https://www.americanprogress.org/issues/education-k-12/reports/2020/10/14/491542/early-high-school-stem-perceptions-associated-postsecondary-outcomes/

Made in the USA
Middletown, DE
25 March 2022